Danger in the Deep

Pat and Julie Balmes

A **PERSPECTIVES** BOOK

Academic Therapy Publications
Novato, California

Art Supervisor: Herb Heidinger
Cover Design and Illustrations: Joe Wallace

International Standard Book Number: 0-87879-320-8

9 8 7 6 5 4 3 2 1 0
6 5 4 3 2 1 0 9 8 7

You'll enjoy all the High Noon Books. Write for
a free complete list of titles.

Contents

CHAPTER 1

Fight for Life

The sea was wild. The day was cold and foggy. Great waves crashed against huge rocks near the shore. White foam splashed into the quiet cove and up onto the beach.

A group of divers in rubber suits waded carefully into the surf. First they lay down on their rubber rafts. Then they kicked with their flippers and moved out into the sea.

The divers worked for the museum. They often went out to catch fish for its tanks. Each diver carried a slurp gun which sucked in fish.

The waves tossed the divers up and down. They dived down to chase fish. Again and again they aimed their gun at a fish and sucked it in. Then they placed the fish in a net tied to their waists. Soon the nets were full, and the divers' tanks were out of air. They waved to one another to return to shore.

Julie Walker was glad. She was a good diver. Her father had taught her to dive when she was little. Mr. Walker worked at the museum. Julie often helped him collect fish and shells.

But now the waves were getting higher, and she was getting tired. She wanted to go back to the beach and take off her heavy diving gear. She lay on her raft and kicked slowly. The other divers swam ahead of her. Mr. Walker wanted the fish brought back quickly so they wouldn't get hurt in the nets.

A sudden big wave tossed Julie off her raft. She sank under the surface of the water. She quickly swam up and gasped for air. But she couldn't stay on top. Something seemed to be dragging her down.

Julie swam up once more. She got her head above water and took a deep breath. Then she felt herself pulled down again. She couldn't get free. What was dragging her deep into the water?

Julie knew she must stay calm. She reached back. She felt something tangled in her diving gear. Seaweed! That ugly kelp, she thought. It floats just under the surface and looks like a bunch of big black snakes.

Stay calm, she told herself. You'll get out of this. But then another big wave crashed over her.

She couldn't breathe. She began choking. The seaweed pulled at her. She became more and more tangled. No matter what she did, she couldn't get loose.

Julie screamed, "Help! Help!" But the wind blew the sound of her cry away. The other divers were too far ahead. They couldn't see or hear her behind them.

But Tom Adams saw her. He was walking along the beach. The cold sea wind on his face and the sand under his bare feet felt good. He had been watching the divers in the water. They were kicking their rafts along to the beach. All but one.

Tom could see that the diver was in trouble. She bobbed up above the surface. Then she went down again. She was near some rocks. Her raft was tossed back and forth by the waves. She couldn't reach it.

He ran along the beach to the spot where the rocks started out into the sea. He climbed up on them and ran toward the diver. When he had gone on the rocks as far as he could, he jumped into the rough water.

It was hard to swim against the huge waves. Finally he reached the raft. He pulled himself up on it and rested a few seconds. He needed to get his strength back. Then he jumped back into the water. He pushed the raft in front of him and swam to the diver.

He couldn't see her head above the water. Was she still alive? "I'm coming. Hold on," he shouted. But she couldn't hear him.

At last — there she was! He pulled her head up above water. She gasped for air. He tried to pull her toward the raft. Something was holding her back. Seaweed!

The seaweed was as big around as a garden hose. Tom tried to untangle it. He couldn't. He saw the knife strapped to Julie's leg. He grabbed it and cut away the seaweed. Then he pushed her up onto the raft. He took off her air tank and weight belt. They quickly sank into the sea. Then he pushed the raft to the rocks. Julie was too weak to climb onto the rocks so Tom helped her. Then he climbed up beside her.

By now the other divers had reached the beach. They looked out at the sea and saw that Julie was in trouble. Some started to swim out again. Others ran out along the rocks.

Julie's father got there first. He made sure she was breathing. He and Tom picked her up and carried her over the jagged rocks.

"I don't know how to thank you," Mr. Walker

said when they got back to the beach. They peeled off Julie's heavy rubber suit. Then they helped her walk to the van and put her in a sleeping bag to get warm.

"You, too," Mr. Walker said to Tom. "You're soaked and chilled. Get out of those wet clothes and into a sleeping bag." He poured hot soup from a thermos. Julie drank it quickly and fell into a deep sleep.

The other divers took off their rubber suits and tossed their diving gear into the van. They put the tanks of fish in, too. Then they all got in for the long drive home.

They were happy that Julie was safe. They thanked Tom again and again. "You ought to be a diver," one said. "You're a good swimmer, and you aren't afraid of the water."

They told Tom stories about diving trips they had taken to find shells and fish for the museum. They told of the fun they had spearfishing and diving for shellfish. They talked about underwater photography and search and salvage work.

"How can I learn to dive?" Tom asked.

"Well, Julie works at Dusty's Dive Shop. They give lessons," her father said with a smile.

CHAPTER 2

Dusty's Dive Shop

Tom called up Julie the next day. "How are you?" he asked.

"I'm OK, thanks to you. You came along just in time."

"Yes, I guess I did. It was just luck that I was walking along the beach. I like to do that. Maybe you'd like to come with me some time."

There was a long silence. Then Julie said, "I'd like to go for a walk with you, Tom. But I don't want to go to the beach."

"How about a hike up the mountain then?" he asked.

"That would be great," Julie answered.

"Fine. I'll come by about ten o'clock Saturday morning," he said.

On Saturday, when Tom got to Julie's house, her mother and father made him feel like an old friend. Mr. Walker showed him pictures and shells from diving trips to the South Seas. Mrs. Walker fixed them a lunch to take on the hike.

Julie was different today. After Tom had pulled her from the sea, she had been scared and quiet. Now she laughed and talked.

"Hey, I thought I was taking out a quiet girl," Tom teased.

"That's because I was scared. I'm usually so noisy, you can't shut me up," she grinned.

As they hiked up the mountain, Julie chatted gaily. But when they stopped to look down at the ocean, she became quiet again.

Tom knew she was thinking about her close call. "Come on. Cheer up," he said.

Julie smiled at him. She could tell that he understood. She made herself start talking again—about her family, friends, school, and the afternoon job at Dusty's Dive Shop.

When they sat down to eat their lunch, Tom told her about wanting to learn to dive. He spoke about his love of the sea. "There's nothing prettier than the sound of fog horns and sea gulls and waves," he said. "I always thought I'd like to work at sea. Be a sailor or a fisherman or a deep-sea diver."

Julie told him more about her job at Dusty's Dive Shop. She fixed diving gear. The gear got hard wear in the salty sea and had to be kept in top shape. Divers' lives depended on it. She liked her little workroom at the back of the shop.

"Come visit me at the shop and meet Dusty. He'll tell you all about the diving lessons," she said.

The next week Tom went to see Julie at the shop. He met Dusty, the owner, who told him about the lessons. "When we think you are ready, you'll have to take an ocean-dive test," Dusty said.

"He's already had an ocean test," joked Julie. She told Dusty how Tom had saved her when she was tangled in the seaweed.

Dusty looked at Tom with interest. "I'd like to hire you, young fellow. We need a man to sell diving gear and to learn how to fix it. Julie can teach you. You can fill people's air tanks and take care of the store. Also, I want you to learn to dive. Then you can help give the diving lessons. If you're the guy who saved Julie, you're the guy I want!"

Wow, thought Tom. What a great chance! "Thanks, Dusty," he said. "I'd love to work for you and learn to dive." And, he thought to himself, I'll see Julie every day. What luck!

The first week at the shop Tom learned how

each piece of diving gear worked. He learned to tell customers which piece of equipment was right for them.

"This is the right mask for you," he told a customer who wore glasses. "You can have your glasses fitted right into this mask. Then you'll be able to see as well under the water as you do on land."

He told another customer, "You can go along when the diving club goes to the beach. You'll be safer if you dive with a group until you learn more about the sport." He pointed to a blackboard where dates and places were listed.

"The club goes to quiet coves along the coast," he said. "There are cliffs on each side of the cove. That keeps the water calm. You can spear fish. You can hunt for shellfish. Or you can ride in our rubber motorboat out to the islands to see the sea birds and seals."

Helping customers made Tom feel good.

CHAPTER 3

Diving Down Deep

When Tom got his first paycheck, he bought diving gear: flippers, a face mask, and a snorkel. He joined the group of beginners in the little pool behind the shop.

The diving teacher, Flip Hartman, showed them how to put on a mask so it wouldn't leak under water. They learned how to swim with the long rubber flippers. The flippers helped them to move through the water faster.

They learned to breathe under the water. At first they used hollow tubes called snorkels to breathe with. They swam just under the surface of the water with the snorkel sticking up into the air. With a snorkel they didn't have to come up for air. They could watch the bottom of the pool and forget about the world above the water.

The students soon learned to swim well using diving gear. They were all surprised at how easy swimming was with a mask, flippers, and snorkel.

A few days later Flip gave them each an air tank. It weighed 35 pounds but was light in the water. It floated because it was full of air. The divers needed weight belts to keep them from floating up to the surface when they were wearing an air tank.

Tom stood in the water and strapped on his tank. He put the air hose in his mouth and breathed in the cold air.

When he wore the tank, Tom could stay under the water for 45 minutes. He moved along the bottom of the pool like a fish.

The other students learned quickly, too. They found that diving with a tank was easy. They didn't get tired. They felt free. It was a great sport.

After a few lessons, everyone was doing well. "We'll go to the beach next Sunday," Flip said. "I'll take you out in the ocean, one at a time. If you can show me that you can use your diving gear safely, I'll give you a Dive Card. Then you can dive any place that you want, even in the South Seas."

On Sunday all of the excited students got to the beach on time. They carried their diving gear.

They scrambled down the steep path to the beach. Some dropped parts of the gear along the way and had to go back for them. Finally all the gear was piled on the beach.

It took a few minutes for everyone to pull on his heavy rubber suit. When they were ready, they looked out at the rough sea. Waves crashed on the cliffs beyond the quiet cove. Then they looked at one another. Would they all be able to pass this important test?

Flip told them that he would test one student at a time. The others were to pair off. He put Tom with a young man whose teeth were chattering. "Don't be afraid. Tom will take care of you," he said.

He warned the students that they should always dive with a partner for safety. Anything could go wrong. Somebody should be there to help. In case of trouble, his air could be shared. "Practice sharing air with your partner while I'm giving the tests," he said.

The divers waded over the slippery rocks. They were careful not to step on their own flippers and fall. When they got into the deep water of the quiet cove, they dived under the water.

It was time to see how well they worked together. Tom's partner pretended he was out of air. Then Tom shared his air hose. They swam slowly under the water. Each took a turn breathing air from the tank.

Finally all of the students had taken their ocean tests but Tom. Flip and Tom got on their rubber floats and kicked out to sea.

When they reached a place deep enough for the test, Flip said, "Tie your float to mine. I'll tie mine to this seaweed."

They were far from shore. High waves carried them up and down. Now Flip would be able to see if Tom could manage his diving gear in the ocean.

Then they dived down 40 feet. Flip took Tom's air hose out of his mouth. They passed it back and forth. They swam close together under the water. At last Flip waved "OK." Tom has passed his ocean test.

By this time Tom was out of air. They worked their way back up to the surface. The waves were still high. It would be hard to swim back using a snorkel. Water would splash in and make breathing hard.

They looked around for their rafts. The rafts were gone! The rope that had tied the rafts to the seaweed had come loose. They had a long, hard swim ahead.

They had two choices. First, the beach which seemed very far away. And next, the cliffs that went out into the sea from the shore. The tired teacher pointed to the cliffs.

Tom nodded yes, and they swam for the cliffs. When they finally reached a rock, Tom climbed up on it. It was hard with the heavy tank on his

Suddenly a wave crashed over him, and he was washed back into the sea.

back. Suddenly a wave crashed over him, and he was washed back into the sea.

Tom and Flip tried again. This time they were able to climb higher before the next wave struck. They were safe now above the waves. They took off their flippers. They climbed higher. Their tanks and weight belts were heavy. They sweated under the suits. The sharp rocks tore the rubber. They were worn out.

When they got to the top of the cliff, they both lay down in the grass. "That was the hardest ocean-dive test I ever gave," joked Flip.

Tom was very tired, but he laughed, too.

CHAPTER 4

A New Adventure

After he passed his ocean test, Tom went to the ocean every weekend. He always asked Julie to come with him.

"I don't want to go diving any more, Tom," she told him sadly. "I was so frightened when the kelp was pulling me down. I never want anything like that to happen to me again."

Tom didn't try to change her mind. He thought about fear. Maybe he could help Julie to get over her fear. He'd look for a way.

He often went to the beach with the dive shop club. Once they dived for abalone, a shellfish. They swam out to the rocks not far from the shore. The rocks were covered wih dark shells as big as a football.

The abalone stuck fast to the jagged rocks. The divers had to use an iron bar to pry them loose. They put a few in their net bags and swam back to shore. On the beach they opened the shells. They were a shining pink inside. The divers took out the white meat and sliced it. Then they fried it over a fire on the beach. Tom thought he had never tasted anything so good.

On another day Tom went with some of the dive shop customers to spearfish. It was easy to get close to the fish. They were not afraid of divers. The divers used spear guns. When they shot at a fish, a spear came out of the gun. Tom had six fish on a string when he swam back to the beach.

On the way home that evening he stopped at Julie's house to give her mother some of the fresh fish. "Stay for dinner, Tom," Mrs. Walker said. "We'll have a fish fry."

Tom was glad to stay. The Walker home was a busy, happy place. Julie's parents worked together in the kitchen. Mr. Walker sharpened his knife and sliced off long pieces of the silver fish. Mrs. Walker coated them in bread crumbs and fried them in garlic and butter.

As they ate, Mr. Walker said, "Tom, you've become a good diver fast. The sea is a wonderful place. There are many beautiful things to see underwater. Things that are different from anything on land. But the best place to see them is where the water is clear and warm."

Mr. Walker talked more about the beauty of the sea and its fish and undersea plants. He seems to be saying that Julie will love the sea again some day, Tom thought. Maybe he has a plan.

Mr. Walker took a sip of coffee and looked at Tom. "I've got an idea. I can't go to the Gulf of California this year to collect shells. Maybe you could do it for me. The museum would pay for the trip. And I'm sure Dusty would give you some time off. Would you do it, Tom?"

"Sure!" said Tom. He was surprised, but the idea sounded great to him.

"That's fine," Mr. Walker said. Then he turned to Julie. "You'd better go along, Julie. Tom will need someone to tell him which shells the museum needs. The shells will have to be properly cleaned, too.

Julie looked down at her plate. She didn't want to go near the water. She hadn't been near the ocean since that awful day when she had almost drowned. But she still had memories of diving in the warm, clear waters of the Gulf. She remembered the fun she had with her father. The amazing fish. The beautiful colors. The hot sun and the blue sky.

She looked into her father's kind eyes. He is trying to help me, she thought. He's trying to help me love the sea again.

"Yes, Dad. I'll go along to help. But I won't dive," she said.

"That's fine. That's just fine," Mr. Walker said. He felt good. His plan was beginning to work.

When Tom went to work at the dive shop the next Monday, he talked to Dusty about going to the Gulf.

"Sure, Tom," Dusty said. "You'll be a better salesman if you've dived in warm water. But it may spoil you for our cold, dark waters here."

In a few weeks summer vacation began, and Julie was out of school. They packed bags with bathing suits, towels, and clothes for the trip home. Another bag held their fins, weight belts, masks, and snorkels. Mr. Walker sent a telegram to the captain of the dive boat saying they were coming. The dive boat would have air tanks for them.

Tom met Julie at her house. He talked to Mr. Walker about the shells the museum wanted. Then they shook hands. "Thanks, Mr. Walker," Tom said. "You're giving me a great trip."

Julie was ready. She wore a T-shirt and blue

jeans, a light jacket, and rubber deck shoes. She looked pretty and happy. They took the bus to the airport. While they waited for their flight to be called, Tom asked, "What's the water like in the Gulf?"

"It's beautiful," Julie answered. "As clear and warm as the air. You can see right down to the sandy bottom. The fish swim up to you. The colors are lovely."

What a lucky guy I am, Tom thought. A vacation with Julie. A chance to swim in the warm waters of the Gulf of California. No heavy rubber suit. No cold wind. No dark freezing water. Just hot sun and clear blue water.

In a few hours their plane touched down on a desert landing strip. They rode a shabby old bus to town. Then they walked to the dock.

There was the dive boat, and it was a rusty old wreck! It needed paint and repairs. But it was big—125 feet long. And it had room for 20 people. Captain Hancock looked strong and tough. He seemed surprised to see them. "Nobody told me you were coming," he growled.

"Didn't you get a telegram? Don't you have room for us?" Tom asked.

"Oh, I'll find a place for you. The girl can sleep with some other women. But you'll have to sleep next to the engines. Take it or leave it." The captain crossed his tattooed arms across his bare chest.

"We'll take it," Tom said. He carried their suitcases onto the boat. A dozen people were sitting on deck laughing and talking. They were happy. Why not? They had a week of cruising, sunning, and swimming ahead.

"After you put your things away," said Captain Hancock, "come back up on deck. We're going to have a party and get to know one another."

The cooks served dinner under a canvas roof on deck. The air had cooled off, and there was a beautiful sunset.

"You're going to have a fine time," the captain said. "We'll go to at least 15 dive spots. We'll move once each day. You'll see amazing fish and underwater plants. I hope you all brought underwater cameras." Then he chatted with his passengers. He bragged a lot about his boat, his cooks, and his own diving skill.

The boat was still tied to the dock. It would sail at night while the passengers slept. It would drop anchor during the day so they could dive.

As Tom sat on deck, he happened to look over at the dock. Three men were standing there.

They were staring at the boat and talking in low voices. They were ragged and barefoot. Tom didn't like their tough look. And he didn't like the way they kept pointing to the dive boat. Suddenly he felt a cold chill.

Later the passengers said goodnight and went to their cabins. They all wanted to be rested and fresh for the first dive the next morning.

Tom hadn't been asleep long before the big engines woke him up. They grated and groaned. Good grief, he thought. How am I going to sleep?

Finally he got up. He picked up his blanket and went out on deck. There he found a quiet spot far from the sound of the engines. He spread his blanket and stretched out on it. He lay there looking up at the stars. No better bed in the world, he thought. The boat rocked him to sleep.

CHAPTER 5

Spearfishing

The next morning at breakfast Tom and Julie met a college student named Dave. Dave knew a lot about life under the sea. He told them what they would find in the Gulf of California. There were many, many kinds of fish.

Julie's eyes were bright as she listened. She remembered the colors and feeling like a mermaid in the strange, beautiful world below. The sky was bright and sunny. The waves looked inviting.

"You come, too," Tom said to her. But Julie shook her head.

Tom told Dave why Julie was afraid. Then Dave and Tom agreed to swim together to be safe. They filled their air tanks and put on their masks and flippers. They picked up their spear guns and climbed down the iron ladder into the sea. As soon as they were underwater, they could see all around them.

The water was full of fish. They swam around slowly looking for food. A school of parrot fish was near. Tom watched them use their hard beaks to chew tiny animals out of the coral. Tom and Dave dove deeper.

Grey manta rays swam around them. They were eight feet across. They were not dangerous, but they looked spooky. The manta rays seemed playful — almost as if they wanted to make friends.

Suddenly Tom saw a 100-pound grouper near the bottom. He pointed it out to Dave. They both dived at the grouper. Tom shot a spear from his gun. But he was too far away. The spear bounced off the fish.

The grouper swam into a cave to hide. Dave went in after him. He shot his spear gun at close range. The spear stuck in the fish. A long rope was tied from the spear to the gun. The grouper swam away from Dave and pulled the spear gun out of his hands.

Tom swam into the cave, too. He aimed his spear gun again and fired. This time the spear went deep into the grouper. As the frantic fish swam to the opening of the cave, it knocked off Dave's mask. It was dragging both spear guns.

Tom and Dave had to swim up to the surface.

The air in their tanks was low. Dave could not see underwater without his mask, so Tom dived back down alone. He spotted the grouper. It was badly hurt. He picked up Dave's spear gun and jammed it into the grouper's mouth like a

Grey manta rays swam around them. They were not dangerous, but they looked spooky.

fishhook. Then he used the gun to pull the grouper to the ship.

Other divers came down the ladder to help pull the big fish on deck. The captain was pleased. "There's enough to feed us all for three days," he said.

Tom went back to look for Dave's mask. He never found it. But he did find some rare shells. He put them in the net bag tied to his waist.

When he brought his bag of shells on deck, all the divers came close to look. Julie pointed out the shell's pictures in her book. The divers learned the names of each kind of shell. They learned which ones were common and which ones were rare.

Julie soaked the shells in alcohol. This killed the animal inside. Then she carefully cleaned out the shell. Her collection was growing.

That evening the divers feasted on the grouper. It tasted great. How good it was to be fed by the sea!

CHAPTER 6

Man-Eater!

The next day they stopped near an island where many seals lived. Tom and Dave swam to the island. Dave walked among the seals. Tom stayed in the water. He speared some small fish. He tied them to his waist with a long string. Then he started to look for shells on the bottom. Shells are hard to find during the day. They dig under the sand and come out to feed at night. Tom was so busy picking up shells, he didn't see the shark. A hammerhead! A man-eater!

Julie saw its fin from the dive boat. The fin slowly swam in circles just above Tom. She screamed. But, of course, Tom couldn't hear her. She spotted a small rubber boat on deck. She tossed it over the side but held onto its long rope so it wouldn't float away. She grabbed a paddle and scrambled down the ladder. She got into the little boat and paddled as fast as she could toward the fin. She wouldn't let herself think about what she was doing. Only that Tom needed help.

Underwater, Tom looked up and saw the shark. Too late, he knew the shark had come for his fish. It sensed blood in the water. Tom untied the string of fish and swam away as fast as he

Underwater, Tom looked up and saw the shark. It sensed blood in the water.

could. The ugly hammerhead made a rush. It gulped down fish and string in one bite. Then it turned and looked at Tom. It wanted to know what Tom was before it attacked him.

Julie could see Tom and the shark through the clear water. She beat the water with the paddle to scare the shark away. Tom looked up and saw the bottom of the boat. He wanted to come up, but he knew the shark would attack him. Sharks think anything on the surface is hurt and helpless.

Quickly Tom swam under the boat. Julie was still beating the water. That would hold off the shark for a minute, Tom thought. He hoped a minute would be long enough. He shot to the surface and pulled himself up and over the side of the little boat. It was hard to do with the heavy tank on his back. The boat rocked. Julie leaned over the other side to balance him.

They watched the shark. It made bigger and bigger circles around the boat. Would it charge the boat? Julie kept beating the water. Was the shark swimming away just to make a rush at them?

They waited. They didn't say a word. The circles grew still bigger. Finally the shark turned and swam away.

Tom took the paddle and headed back to the dive boat. "Thanks, Julie," he said. "It's my turn to thank you for saving my life." He grinned at her. "The shark ate my fish," he said, "so what's for lunch?"

Julie grinned back at him. "Not you!" she said. It was easy to laugh now that the danger was past.

During lunch Tom told about how brave Julie had been. The divers were worried by the story of the shark. One of them asked the captain to move to a new spot.

Captain Hancock laughed at them. "Sharks have never hurt anybody around here," he said. "Just go to the other side of that seal island if you're afraid. If you see any hammerheads, take their picture."

"Why are they called hammerheads?" asked one of the passengers.

"Because their heads look like two hammers back to back. Ugly devils," said Captain Hancock.

After lunch the divers took the rubber boat and paddled to the island. They stayed there a long time, looking at the seals. Finally they went into the water on the other side of the island.

As soon as they were underwater, they were sorry. They saw many hammerheads. One big shark rushed them. Luckily they were close to the island. The shark chased them out of the water and up on the beach.

When they got back to the boat, they told the captain about the shark attack. They demanded that he move the boat to a new spot.

"All right," said Captain Hancock. "But you're a bunch of sissies."

"We don't see you swimming with sharks," said a diver. He sounded angry.

"I'm the best diver here. I can prove it. I'll show you I can stay down longer than any of you," said the Captain.

"I'll bet you can't," said a woman. She had dived in three oceans.

"Yes, I can," said the captain. "Here's five dollars that says I can. Do you want to bet?"

"Yes, I'll bet," she said. "I can stay down two minutes.""

"Who else wants to bet?" asked Captain Hancock. He soon had a hatful of five dollar bills. Then he matched their money with his own.

"There's a spot I know that's real pretty. We'll go there. You can show me how long you can stay down," he said.

CHAPTER 7

Night Dive

The dive boat sailed for most of the day. The divers were excited about the contest. When the anchor dropped, they hurried down the ladder. They took snorkels, not tanks. This was a test to see who could stay down longest without an air tank.

The captain and Julie stayed on deck. "Now, Julie, hold the stopwatch. We'll see who can stay down longest." Then he shouted, "Everybody down." They all dived in.

Soon they began to pop up. They spouted water from their snorkels. Each one asked, "How long was I down?" Julie wrote down each diver's time.

Dave was the last one to come up. He had stayed down two and a half minutes. Then the captain shouted, "Now you're going to see some real diving." He climbed upon the boat rail. Then he made a swan dive off the high deck.

He came up spouting water. "Now get ready for the longest dive you'll ever see," he shouted. And he dived deep.

On deck Julie counted. One minute. Two minutes. Three minutes. The captain was still down! Three and a half minutes! Then he splashed up through the water.

The divers stared at him. They couldn't believe it. Back on deck, the captain took the money he had won. He grinned at them and went to his cabin to put the money away.

"Nobody can stay down three and a half minutes," growled the woman who had dived in three oceans.

The divers spent the afternoon catching small lobsters that walked along the sandy bottom. They had a lobster dinner that night.

"Does anyone want to go on a dive tonight?" Captain Hancock asked at dinner.

The divers all liked the idea. They would take underwater flashlights. They knew that fish and plants feed at night.

After the sun went down, the divers put on tanks. Each diver had a flashlight. Julie looked down into the dark water. "I'm glad I'm not diving," she said.

But Dave and Tom were glad they were going. They could hardly wait to slide under the water. They went down deep in the glow of their flashlights.

The water was a warm 84 degrees. Fish swam up to them. Suddenly a dark shape swam just outside their light. What was it? Not another shark, Tom hoped. A big sea turtle swam slowly into the light. Dave reached out. He grabbed the front of its big shell as it went by. He had to drop his flashlight. Still glowing, it sank to the dark bottom. The sea turtle was four feet wide. It pulled Dave along. What fun! But finally Dave had to let go. The turtle was pulling him away into the darkness.

Dave was alone in the black water without a light. Or was he? He moved his hand back and forth. A little shower of glittering specks lit up. He moved his hand again. And again the tiny sea life glowed like fireflies.

Dave looked down and saw his flashlight. It was still lit. He dived for it. Then he looked around for the others. He saw their flashlights glowing. He swam toward the light and met Tom.

They followed the others through the opening of an undersea cave. It was a world of colorful fish and coral. Reds and yellows. They swam inside. It was bright as day with so many flashlights. The cave was full of fish. The most beautiful fish Tom had ever seen. Big speckled bass, all colors of the rainbow. Too beautiful to shoot.

Tom kept his eye on the opening. He knew it was easy to get lost in an underwater cave. He looked up at the roof. It was covered with shining little rare shells. He had seen them in Julie's book. What a find! They were the kind Julie's father wanted for the museum. He pulled them off the roof of the cave and put them in his bag.

CHAPTER 8

Pirates

The captain was in a good mood at breakfast the next morning. But the woman who dived in three oceans said, "I know how you stayed down so long. I saw the air pockets at the top of the underwater cave last night. You swam into the cave and took a breath from an air pocket."

"Now, lady," said Captain Hancock. "Don't say I cheated." But there was a grin on his face.

All the divers wanted their money. But the captain wouldn't give it back. Instead he said that he would tell them a secret. He knew where there were pearl beds. He would take them there the next day.

"You mean there are still pearls in the Gulf of California?" asked one man. "I thought the pearls were all gone a long time ago."

"There are still pearls here. I'm going to show you where," the captain said.

In the morning everybody went for a swim at the new dive spot. Tom and Dave went spear-fishing. But first they looked around carefully for sharks. When they speared a fish, they put it in a rubber boat so no blood was in the water. When they had enough fish to feed everybody, they collected more shells.

After lunch the captain moved the boat near an island. He dropped anchor in its peaceful cove. This time the captain would dive, too. "I'll show you where the pearl beds are," he said.

They all put on their diving gear. "It's too bad you don't want to dive, Julie. Maybe we could find a pearl," Tom said. He thought a pearl would be the right reward for courage.

But Julie shook her head. "No, you go," she said. "Everyone else is going."

Tom thought that over. It would be nice to have some time alone with Julie. "I'll stay on the boat and help you clean shells," he said.

Tom and Julie enjoyed the peace and quiet of the boat after being with lots of people. Suddenly Julie pointed. "What's that?" she asked.

Tom shaded his eyes. A small motorboat was coming toward them. Three men were in it. Soon it was tied to the tall dive boat. One man yelled up at Tom, "Lower your ladder. We're police.

We want to inspect your boat." He was wearing parts of a uniform, but he didn't look like a policeman. The other two men were also dressed in parts of police uniforms.

Those are the guys I saw on the dock the first night, Tom thought. I didn't like their looks then, and I don't like them now. They look more

A small motorboat was coming. Three men were in it, one wearing parts of a uniform.

like pirates than policemen.

"I said lower your ladder," the leader said again. When Tom didn't move, the leader pulled out a pistol. He waved it at Tom. "We're coming aboard."

No way, Tom thought. I'll pretend I didn't hear them. "Julie," he shouted so the men could hear him, "it's hot. Get some cold beer for these men."

Julie looked scared, but she did as he told her to. Tom looked down at the motorboat. He saw that the current was flowing away from the dive boat. If he could untie the rope, the motorboat would drift away on the current. But first he'd have to wreck its motor.

When Julie came back with the beer, Tom shouted to the men, "Here's your beer." He let down the cans of beer in a bucket. Two of the men sat down to drink their beer.

Again the leader cried out, "Lower your ladder."

Again Tom pretended he didn't understand. "Hey, Julie," he said loudly, "these men are hungry. Get some sandwiches." He took her arm and led her away from the rail. He was worried about her. The leader might start shooting.

CHAPTER 9

The Net

"Julie," Tom whispered. "I've got a plan. Take a net. Go down the other side of the boat so they can't see you. Be very quiet so they don't hear you splash. I'll keep them busy. Swim underwater to the motorboat. Dive down under it. Wrap the net around the motor's blades."

Julie understood. She had seen the current flowing away from the dive boat. If the motorboat was untied, it would drift away. And without a motor, the men couldn't come back.

She nodded at Tom. She picked up a net and walked to the other side of the boat. She looked down at the water. She remembered the day she had nearly drowned.

I've got to do this, she thought. Those men will come aboard. They've got a gun. I can't just stand here and let that happen. Quietly she slipped into the water.

Now all the men were shouting at Tom. I need a new idea, he thought. Then it came to him. "We've found some big pearls," he shouted. "Do you want to see them?" He put some broken shells in the bottom of a bucket. He let the bucket down on a rope. He banged the bucket against the boat as he let it down. He made a lot of noise. He didn't want the men to hear Julie.

Suddenly Tom let the bucket drop. It spilled into the motorboat. The men began looking around in the bottom of their motorboat. "I don't see any pearls," the leader growled.

"Oh, yes, I see one. Look there," Tom shouted. He leaned over the rail and pointed to the leader's feet. All three men looked down, and at that instant Tom untied their boat.

"This is the last time I'm going to tell you. Lower the ladder—NOW," the leader shouted. He waved his pistol in the air. Then he saw that his motorboat was beginning to drift away from the dive boat. He tried to start the motor. It made a funny grinding noise. Then it stopped.

"Something's wrong. Dive down and look," he said to the other men.

"Oh, no. Not on your life. Too many sharks," they answered.

Tom didn't want them to look into the water

and spot Julie, so he laughed at them. He laughed as loud as he could. The leader jumped up and down in a rage. He shot at Tom. He missed. Tom ducked behind a cabin.

By this time Julie was climbing up the other side of the dive boat on a rope ladder. "Great job, Julie," Tom said. "Stay down low and keep

"Lower the ladder—NOW." He waved his pistol in the air.

quiet. The current will do the rest."

Tom and Julie stood behind the cabin and watched the motorboat slowly drift away. They could hear the angry men shouting at one another.

The divers, who had been looking for pearls, heard the shot. But by the time they got back to the dive boat, the motorboat had drifted far away.

Tom told the captain about the men who said they were policemen. "Oh, no, they weren't," said Captain Hancock. "They were pirates. If they had come aboard, they would have taken over my boat. And then they would have sailed it to South America and sold it. It happens a lot in these waters."

"But what would they have done with us?" Julie asked.

"Put you off on an island. You wouldn't have lasted long. The sun is boiling hot. There's no water on the islands. But there are rattlesnakes. It would have been murder!"

Julie told them how Tom had fooled the men. Then Tom told how Julie had dived under the motorboat to wrap the net around the motor's blades.

"I thought you didn't have much to say," the

captain said to Tom. "But you can really talk your way out of trouble." He turned to Julie. "And you, young lady. I thought you were afraid to dive."

"I was," said Julie.

"But she's not afraid any more," Tom said. He smiled at her. "How about you and I going after some pearls?"

"Why not?" she said with a grin.

They put on their diving gear and went down the ladder. As they sank into the clear, warm water, a school of amberjack swam toward them. It looked like a wall of silver fish coming to say hello. When the fish were almost near enough to touch, they turned away. Hundreds of them flashed by.

Tom and Julie could see all around and 200 feet down to the sandy bottom. It was a strange and beautiful world. Tom took Julie's hand. She was no longer afraid, he knew.

They swam away from the dive boat to the pearl beds near the island. Maybe they'd find a pearl. Maybe not. Who cares, thought Tom. I'll settle for a long underwater swim. It's the greatest show on earth!